**Printed and published in Great Britain by
D. C. Thomson & Co., Ltd., 185 Fleet Street, London EC4A 2HS.
© D. C. THOMSON & CO., LTD., 2001.**
(Certain stories do not appear exactly as originally published.)

ISBN 0 85116 771 3

HISTORY OF FUN

FROM THE **BEANO** AND THE **DANDY**

STONEHENGE

BIG UGGY: DENNIS THE MENACE:
BASH STREET KIDS: MINNIE THE MINX:
THREE BEARS: LORD SNOOTY:
DENNIS THE MENACE: ALF WIT.

NORTH MAN

CORPORAL CLOT:
WONDER BOY: BIFFO THE BEAR:
DENNIS THE MENACE:
DIRTY DICK.

HADRIAN'S WALL

JULIUS SNEEZER: DREAMY DANIEL:
DENNIS THE MENACE/SMASHER:
BRASSNECK:
BASH STREET KIDS.

MAGNA CARTA

JIMMY'S MAGIC PATCH: SMASHER:
PANSY POTTER: KORKY THE CAT:
BIG HEAD AND THICK HEAD:
DENNIS THE MENACE: SIR LAUGHALOT.

COLUMBUS

LITTLE PLUM:
SPOOFER McGRAW.

SPANISH ARMADA

JONAH: BASH STREET KIDS:
MINNIE THE MINX:
BIFFO THE BEAR:
BULLY BEEF AND CHIPS.

The Beano and The Dandy (with help from The Topper, The Beezer and The Sparky comics which are no longer with us) will show on the following pages how History need not be as boring as you may think!

Did Little Plum discover America? Was Corporal Clott really a Viking? What did Desperate Dan look like with a 'Beatle Cut' hairstyle? How did Lord Snooty knock a war-time German Zeppelin out of the sky? The answers to all these, and lots more, lie in this latest collection of pages from past ages!

MR BUBBLES:
WUZZY WIZ:
TOAD IN THE HOLE.

JIMMY'S MAGIC PATCH:
BASH STREET KIDS:
WILD YOUNG DIRKY:
PLUM MACDUFF: THE McTICKLES.

BALL BOY: DENNIS THE MENACE:
THREE BEARS: KORKY THE CAT:
JIMMY'S MAGIC PATCH:
2-GUN TONY.

DREAMY DANIEL: DENNIS THE MENACE:
SMUDGE: BARON VON REICHS-PUDDING:
HUNGRY HORACE:
BING BANG BENNY.

LORD SNOOTY:
DREAMY DANIEL:
BIFFO THE BEAR:
BASH STREET KIDS AND PUPS.

CORPORAL CLOTT:
NICK KELLY:
DESPERATE DAN:
LITTLE PLUM.

ELIZABETH I

GREAT FIRE OF LONDON

BATTLE OF TRAFALGAR

QUEEN VICTORIA

WINSTON CHURCHILL

MOON LANDING

Beezer
HEY DAYS
STONEHENGE

WAS this how Stonehenge appeared in its hey day—massive and mighty, its towering standing stones casting long shadows across Salisbury Plain? Although no one can say for certain, experts now believe that it did look like this. But who built Stonehenge? When? And why? For centuries, the answers to these questions remained unknown. But bit by bit, some of the answers were pieced together. From excavations, and study of the stones themselves, it was discovered that they were erected by men of the New Stone Age and the Bronze Age, more than three thousand years ago. This meant that Stonehenge was built before the discovery of the wheel—yet some of the stones could only have been found in South Wales, more than 200 miles away, and even the heaviest stones, weighing 40 tons and more, must have been manhandled for at least 20 miles! For what reason, then, did these primitive people slave over such a task? Was Stonehenge a court? A burial place? A sun temple? To this day, no one really knows . . . .

FOR hundreds of years, the standing stones of Stonehenge, on Salisbury Plain, have mystified the world . . . . . .

Look carefully and you may see Big Uggy!
Or has he gone to the next page already?

In the beginning there was ... Big Uggy with his dinosaur pal Dopeydokus, whose comic career was set in stone in the pages of the Topper from 1958 to 1962. This clever little prehistoric caveman's escapades were certainly ahead of their time!

BIG UGGY

The 3 Bears didn't actually live in Stone Age times, but their forebears did — in the very

Here's a FANGtastic Gnasher Tale from thirty years ago!

North Man

From out of the frozen Northlands long ago came a man to strike terror into the hearts of other men. Bearded and befurred against the cold of his northern haunts, and sailing the oceans in his open boats, he made incredible voyages, and raided and pillaged the coastlines of the world. Few could stand against this fierce blue-eyed warrior who seemed to know no fear. He worshipped the stern gods of war, and when he died, asked only that he go to Valhalla, where he and his comrades could fight all day, and feast all night. He was the North Man.

FACES OF MAN Nº 1

FROM THE
SPARKY BOOK 1975

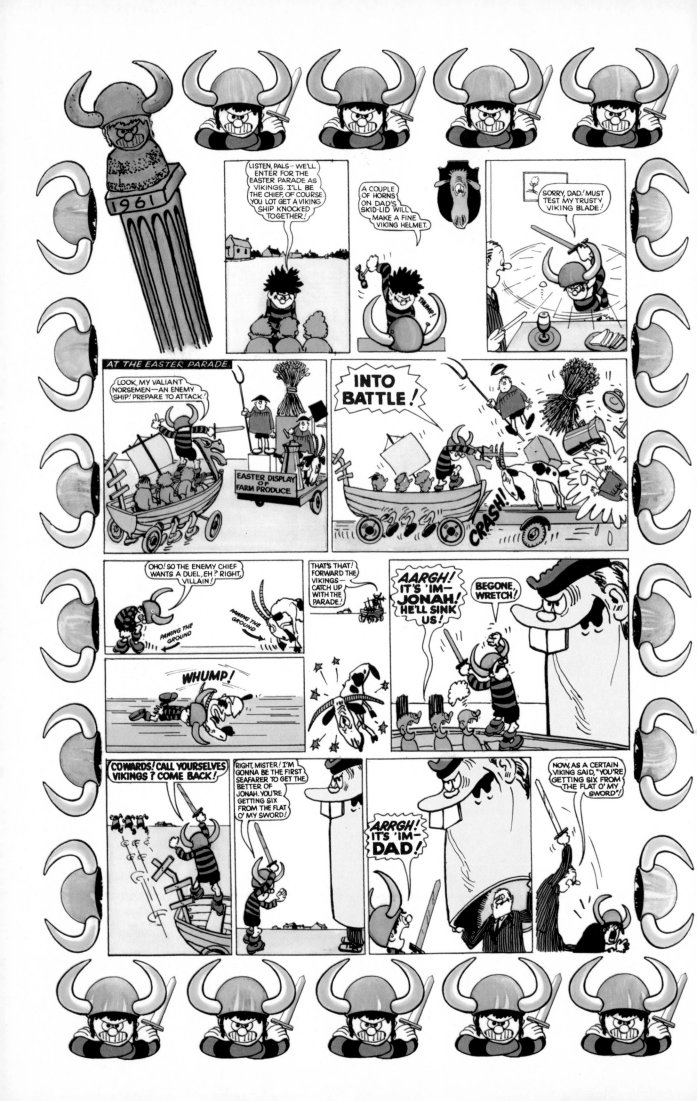

THIS is Hadrian's Wall as it stands today, ancient relic of an ancient empire . . . . .

FROM THE
BEEZER BOOK 1962

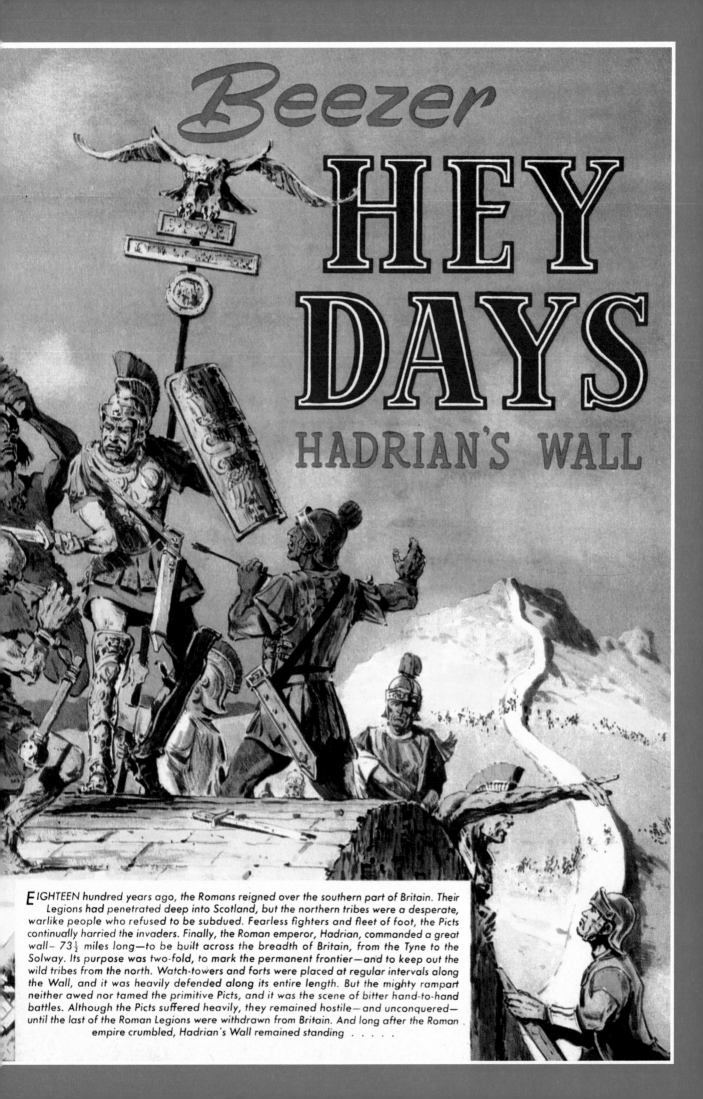

Beezer
HEY DAYS
HADRIAN'S WALL

EIGHTEEN hundred years ago, the Romans reigned over the southern part of Britain. Their Legions had penetrated deep into Scotland, but the northern tribes were a desperate, warlike people who refused to be subdued. Fearless fighters and fleet of foot, the Picts continually harried the invaders. Finally, the Roman emperor, Hadrian, commanded a great wall— 73½ miles long—to be built across the breadth of Britain, from the Tyne to the Solway. Its purpose was two-fold, to mark the permanent frontier—and to keep out the wild tribes from the north. Watch-towers and forts were placed at regular intervals along the Wall, and it was heavily defended along its entire length. But the mighty rampart neither awed nor tamed the primitive Picts, and it was the scene of bitter hand-to-hand battles. Although the Picts suffered heavily, they remained hostile—and unconquered— until the last of the Roman Legions were withdrawn from Britain. And long after the Roman empire crumbled, Hadrian's Wall remained standing . . . . .

HERE was something that attracted Chuckler Charley Brand and his amazing metal pal, Brassneck. A contest to find the best-decorated lorry! Charley fancied taking part in that!

DECORATED ✱ FLOAT PARADE
CASH PRIZE AND SILVER CUP TO WINNERS
ALL ENTRIES ✱✱ WELCOME

LET'S GO AND SEE CYRIL CRABTREE. HIS DAD OWNS A LOT OF LORRIES.

BRASSNECK

Disappointment for the chums. Cyril Crabtree refused to let Brassneck and Charley near his float.

CRABTREE'S TRANSPORT DEPARTMENT

COULDN'T WE HELP ON YOUR FLOAT, CYRIL?

CERTAINLY NOT! WE DON'T WANT SCRUFF LIKE YOU SPOILING OUR CHANCES OF WINNING!

Undaunted, the chums went along to the town dump and proceeded to build their own float. They were watched jealously by Cyril Crabtree and one of his pals, Sniffler Perkins.

GEE! THIS IS A SMASHING FLOAT WE'RE BUILDING, BRASSNECK!

TOWN DUMP

LOOK! CHARLEY BRAND AND HIS METAL PAL HAVE BUILT SOME SORT OF ENGINE! IT LOOKS RATHER GOOD. WE'LL HAVE TO DO SOMETHING ABOUT IT!

1965

As soon as they saw their chance, Cyril and Sniffler nipped across and gave the home-made float and good hard shove down a slope.

HEY! LEAVE THAT ALONE!

QUICK! PUSH HARD BEFORE THEY CAN STOP US!

HEE-HEE!

OH, NO!

THE MARTIANS HAVE LANDED—OR SOMETHING!

With Brassneck and Charley racing after it, the home-made float smashed to smithereens at the foot of the hill. It was a total wreck. All the work of the chums had gone for nothing.

Sadly, the chums wandered home. But on the way they met Big Jim, the coalman. He had a problem, too.

SANDY'S GOT A NAIL IN HIS FOOT!

Charley made a deal with Big Jim.

IF WE HELP YOU, WOULD YOU LEND US YOUR CART FOR THE AFTERNOON?

RIGHTO, CHARLEY!

Using his extending teeth, Brassneck gripped the nail and then jerked his head back. Out popped the nail!

EASY DOES IT!

The next job was to deliver Big Jim's load and Brassneck and Charley worked like demons to get the job done fast.

ONLY TWENTY BAGS TO GO, LADS!

GOSH! THIS IS A HEAVY ONE!

As soon as the coal had been unloaded, the chums set to work scrubbing the cart clean.

MAKE SURE YOU CLEAN OFF EVERY SPECK OF COALDUST, BRASSNECK!

Charley's bright idea was to decorate the cart to represent a Roman chariot. The job had just been completed when who should appear but Cyril on his float!

THAT'LL PUT A STOP TO YOU!

CRABTREE'S TRANSPORT

Cyril threw a squib down near Sandy. The horse reared in fear and Brassneck lost his reins.

here's not much history — just a lot of Brassneck!

Panic-stricken, Sandy stampeded down the road. Brassneck and Charley hung on tight.

QUICK! DO SOMETHING, BRASSNECK!

As the cart swept along, it crashed into a painter's scaffolding. Before they knew what was happening, the painter and his mate got a big let-down.

WOW! WE'RE GOING TO HAVE A COUPLE OF PASSENGERS!

On thundered the cart. Then, just ahead, Constable Crumlin signalled the cart to stop.

CARNIVAL

HALT! IN THE NAME OF THE LAW!

WHAT DOES HE THINK WE ARE, MAGICIANS?

HELP!

Constable Crumlin seized the horse's reins, but he was swept off his feet.

Brassneck dragged the bemused bobby aboard the chariot.

UP YOU COME!

Round the next bend, two billposters were busy outside the Roxy Cinema—blissfully unaware of the approaching disaster.

ROXY CINEMA

IT'S BEEN A NICE, QUIET DAY, BERT!

YES! JUST ONE MORE POSTER AND IT WILL BE KNOCKING OFF TIME.

AYEE!

Next second, Sandy thundered up. The billposters were hurled up into the air and on to the cart. And the poster wrapped itself round Brassneck and streamed away behind.

JUST WAIT TILL I GET MY NOTEBOOK OUT!

Then Brassneck had a great idea. The metal marvel made his arms shoot out on long springs. Now he was able to reach the dangling reins.

NOW LET ME SEE—THE CHARGES ARE—FAILING TO STOP AT A HALT SIGN, ASSAULT AND BATTERY, KIDNAPPING A POLICE OFFICER...

WELL DONE, BRASSNECK!

OH! WHAT AN AMUSING FLOAT! THAT'S WORTH A PRIZE!

Tugging with all his strength, Brassneck dragged Sandy to a halt—right in front of the judges. They were most impressed!

To thunderous applause from all the spectators, Charley and Brassneck were awarded the cup. Everyone was pleased—except for Cyril Crabtree and Sniffler Perkins, of course!

FANCY CONSTABLE CRUMLIN TRYING TO MAKE CHARGES AGAINST THE WINNERS. I HAD TO TEAR UP HIS NOTEBOOK!

CONGRATULATIONS, LADS! HERE'S THE CUP! YOU DESERVE IT!

BAH! CHARLEY BRAND AND HIS METAL PAL HAVE WON AFTER ALL!

What would Bash Street School life be like back in Roman times? Find out in this story from . . .

MDCCCCLXXII

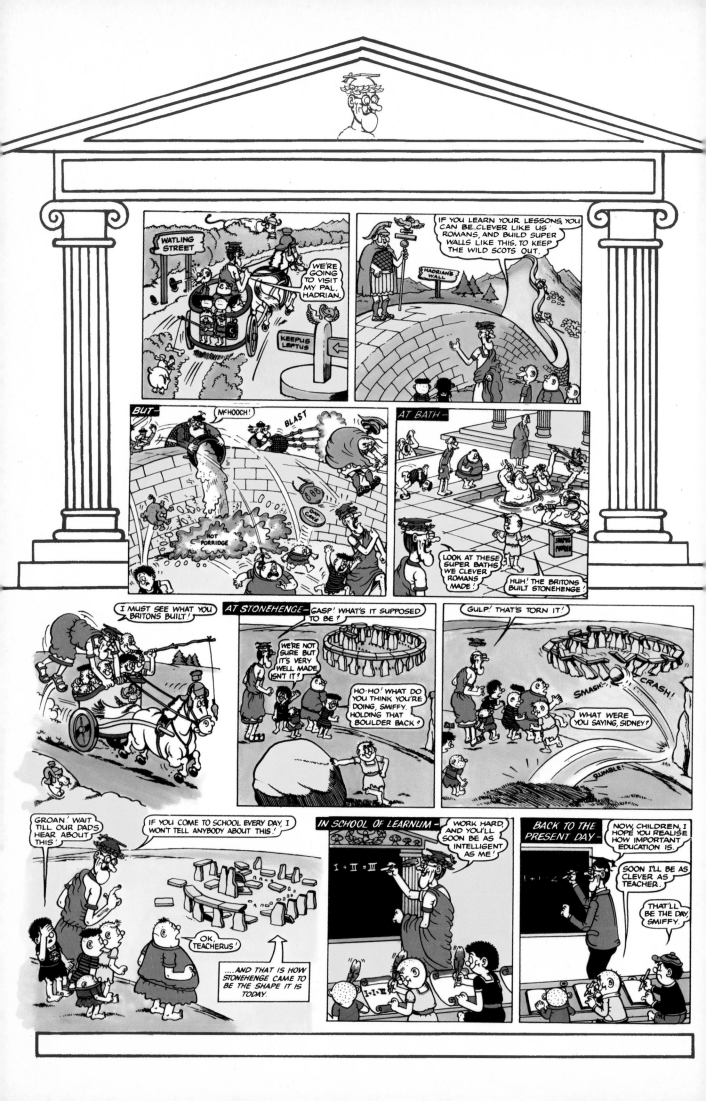

Dennis Ye Menace

Dennis is a household name—
You all know this wild lad.
He's always being spanked because
His hobby's being bad!
Now if he lived in by-gone days,
D'you think he would be good?
Let's whisk the Menace back through time
To meet bold Robin Hood . . .

IN far-off times there lived a young knave by the name of Dennis ye Menace. He was known throughout the length and breadth of the land for all his naughty deeds.

His father was a poor man—he was bound to be with a son like Dennis—and he worked as a cobbler in the town of Nottingham.

One morning, as ye Menace set off to school, his mother spake to him.

"Be a good little varlet, Dennis, and don't push ye Headmaster in ye Ducke Ponnde."

"Worry ye not, mother," chirped the boy. "I won't bother ye Headmaster today."

As he trotted off down the highway, the little knave sniggered to himself.

"Heh! Heh! That's because I'm going to play ye truante."

So saying, Dennis ye Menace turned off the highway and nipped into the Forest of Sherwood, in which lived the famous outlaw, Robin Hood, and his Merrie Men.

After a time, ye Menace saw a large man come out of the woods and start to cross a stream by a fallen tree trunk.

"Forsooth!" gasped ye Menace. "'Tis Little John, one of Robin Hood's band of merrie outlaws. I'll have some sport with the fellow!"

Whereupon the lad produced a pea-shooter from his doublet and fired a salvo at Little John.

"OOYAH! I've been stung," bellowed Little John, leaping in the air.

When he came down, he discovered—alas!— that he had missed the tree-trunk. SPLASH!

Little John squelched away through the forest, and ye Menace followed him at a distance.

As the dripping figure of Little John walked into the camp, he was met by roars of laughter from Robin Hood and his outlaws.

"Forsooth! They will not be so merrie when I am finished with them!" quoth ye Menace in his perch high on the bough of an old oak tree.

One of the outlaws, a tall man dressed in red, laughed louder than anybody.

WHACK

WHOP

WHACK

WHAM

"Watch it, Will Scarlett," bellowed Little John, "or I will bash thee on ye bonce with my trusty quarter-staff!"

Suddenly Will Scarlett went red in the face, for a juicy tomato had come whizzing out of nowhere and smote him hard.

It was now Little John's turn to laugh.

"Haw! Haw!" he cackled. "Now thy face matches thy red jerkin, good Will!"

The outlaws rocked with laughter. But the merriment ceased when a bag of itching powder burst in their midst. Within a minute the clearing was filled with writhing, scratching outlaws, each one now far from merrie!

Dennis laughed so much he fell out of his tree. —and landed right on top of Robin Hood.

"OOYAH!" howled Robin. "Aha! Now I see the varlet who has been playing jokes on us!"

At once Robin Hood and his sad band took ye Menace back to his father's humble cottage.

"Ho, good cobbler!" quoth Robin. "This lad of thine hath given me more trouble than ye Sheriffe of Nottingham. No longer are my Merrie Men merrie."

Dennis's Dad immediately seized a pair of deerskin slippers which he had just finished.

"Worry ye not, bold Robin," quoth he. "This is as good a tyme as any to test ye slippers for ye toughness."

Robin and his men looked puzzled.

"I will, of course," continued Dennis's Dad, "test ye slippers on ye seat of ye doublet of ye son!"

At such a joyful jest, Robin and the outlaws roared with laughter.

And so the Merrie Men were merrie once more and, as they rode back into Sherwood Forest, a stirring sound rang out from the cobbler's cottage.

WHACK! WHACK! WHACK!

If you pass by Dad's house today,
You'll hear that self-same noise
As spanks galore are given to
The wildest of wild boys!

from BEANO BOOK 1964

MAGIC MOMENTS

THE SIGNING OF THE MAGNA CARTA

EARLY in England's history came a moment that was to have effects lasting to the present day. In 1215, monarchs had absolute power over their subjects, and King John, the ruler of that day, was a hated tyrant. At last he was brought before an assembly of nobles on an island in the Thames, near Runnymede. There he was made to sign the Great Charter, or Magna Carta. This historic document pledged certain rights to the people of England.

It could be said that from this occasion rose Britain's present democratic system of government, housed on the banks of the same River Thames, at Westminster.

FROM THE
BEEZER BOOK 1966

JIMMY AND HIS MAGIC PATCH

1 — Jimmy Watson's Grannie wasn't feeling well enough to do her washing, so Ma Watson sent Jimmy to fetch it. Jimmy bundled the dirty washing, clothes pegs, clothes pole and other washing gear into an old pram and pushed off until he came to the top of a hill — and then he sat in the pram and free-wheeled. With the long clothes pole held like a lance Jimmy began to imagine he was a knight — and next minute he wished he was back in the Middle Ages.

2 — Whizz! The pram took off and Jimmy soared back to days of old when knights were bold and suits were made of tin. The Magic Patch on Jimmy's pants had answered Jimmy's wish and in the wink of an eye he was landing in a field laid out for a tournament. Two knights on horseback were fighting a grim duel with lances and Jim could see that one of the knights was in deadly peril. His lance was broken and his opponent, in black armour, was galloping towards him.

3 — The wheels of Jimmy pram hit the turf and he careered forward to meet the oncoming knight. Ther were no brakes on Jimmy's pram and he couldn't stop it. Our pal held his clothes pole lance firmly in front of him and with a terrific jar it connected with the Black Knight's chin!

1949

4 — The half-stunned knight toppled in the dust while the spectators in the marquee at the side laughed their heads off. Meanwhile the knight with the broken lance dismounted and clapped Jimmy on the back. "Sir Gerard's my name, lad," he chuckled. "Make fast your carriage to my horse and we'll be off."

5 — Jimmy climbed up behind Sir Gerard and off they went, leaving the Black Knight nursing a swollen jaw and vowing vengeance. "I'll settle with that young pup for making a fool of me," he said nastily. "I'll boil him in oil." And the Black Knight made his plans. Half an hour later as Jimmy and his pals were riding through a wood, armed men sprang from hiding.

6 — It was the Black Knight and his men. They had ridden swiftly ahead and lain in wait in the wood. Strong arms grabbed Jimmy while a heavy yeoman dropped from the trees and put Jim's pal out of action. "To the castle with them!" roared the Black Knight. Jimmy and Sir Gerard were borne off and locked up behind bars in the Black Knight's fortress.

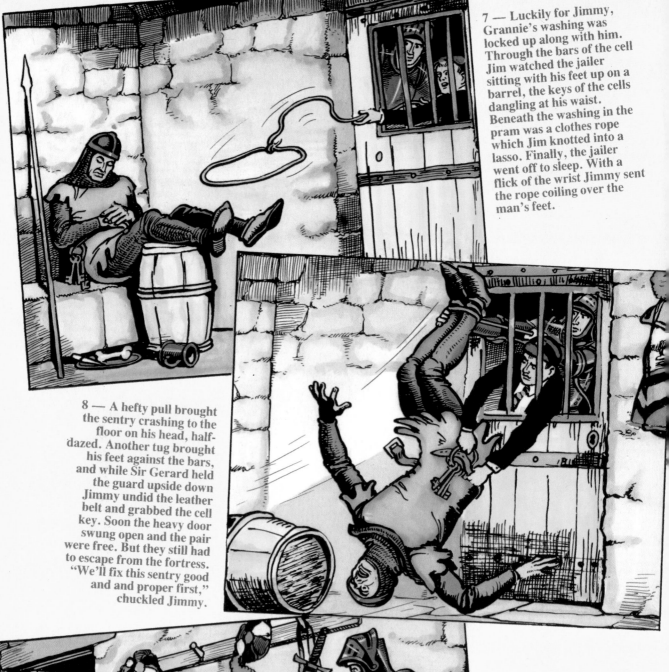

7 — Luckily for Jimmy, Grannie's washing was locked up along with him. Through the bars of the cell Jim watched the jailer sitting with his feet up on a barrel, the keys of the cells dangling at his waist. Beneath the washing in the pram was a clothes rope which Jim knotted into a lasso. Finally, the jailer went off to sleep. With a flick of the wrist Jimmy sent the rope coiling over the man's feet.

8 — A hefty pull brought the sentry crashing to the floor on his head, half-dazed. Another tug brought his feet against the bars, and while Sir Gerard held the guard upside down Jimmy undid the leather belt and grabbed the cell key. Soon the heavy door swung open and the pair were free. But they still had to escape from the fortress. "We'll fix this sentry good and and proper first," chuckled Jimmy.

9 — Jimmy dived into the depths of the pram and brought out two bars of soap. While Sir Gerard gagged and bound the jailer, Jimmy lashed the soap to the sentry's feet. "That's fixed the jailer, but now what?" muttered Jimmy. Sir Gerard pointed to a suit of page-boy's clothing, hanging on a peg nearby. Jimmy quickly tumbled to what Sir Gerard wanted.

10 — Meanwhile the Black Knight and his men were busy feeding their ugly faces at a long table in the banqueting hall. Disguised as a page-boy Jimmy strolled around exploring the castle and he soon found out that there was only one way of escape — through the banqueting hall. "I'll fix this," muttered Jim, and he nipped back to the pram for a clothes peg.

11 — Not one of the hungry ruffians round the table knew what Jimmy was up to as he knelt swiftly behind the Black Knight and used the clothes peg to fasten the tail of the bully's black tunic to the corner of the table-cloth. Jimmy sprang up sharply. Then he lifted a tureen of soup from the table and tipped steaming liquid over the Black Knight.

12 — The Black Knight darted from the table and took the table-cloth with him. Everything on it went up in the air. In the uproar Jimmy and Sir Gerard made for the door and freedom. Jimmy didn't have much time before the Magic Patch tugged him back home again but he had the feed of his young life at Sir Gerard's castle before he went!

Jimmy Watson gets everywhere, thanks to his Magic Patch! There's thirteen years between Jimmy's meeting with William Tell and his son, and Smasher's 1959 tale — but which is the better 'Tell tale'?!

THE SMASHER

In Wonderland, Pansy Potter is 'hooping' for joy, because she soon has the dragon in a spin, thanks to King Arthur's Round Table.

ights which were more than a year apart certainly had folk in a "daze"!

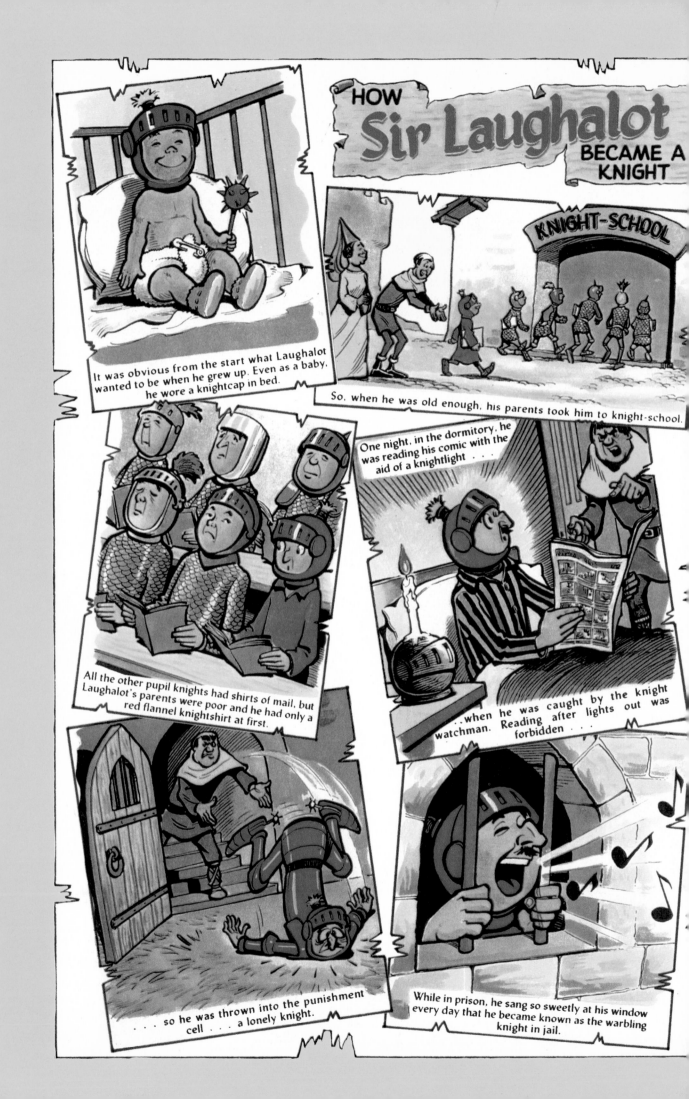

YEARS TO REMEMBER-
1492

FROM THE
SPARKY BOOK 1972

TO the natives, the three battered sailing ships approaching their West Indian island were like something from another world.

To the sailors, the island WAS another world.

For with their leader, Christopher Columbus, they had set out from the "Old World" 70 days earlier, to find a new route to Asia.

Instead they had discovered the New World of the Americas. The year was 1492.

He was the biggest fibber in the whole of the Sparky Comic for a hundred years (and that's a fib!) Believe it or not, this silly tale from Spoofer McGraw is from Sparky 1974.

ONE DAY, DOWN AT THE DOCKS—

HMM! MUST BE ONE SOMEWHERE!

ONE WHAT, BO, OL' SON?

AH! ONE ANCHOR! WHO INVENTED 'EM?

OH, THAT WAS OL' CHRISTOPHER COLUMBUS. YOU KNOW – THE BLOKE WHO DISCOVERED AMERICA!

TRIP!

THUD!

AN' BEIN' A JEALOUS SORT OF WHALE, HE KEPT CHASIN' THE OTHER WHALES AWAY– ONLY MOST OF THE TIME THEY WERE ACTUALLY SHIPS...

GET OUT OF MY TERRITORY, WHALE!

WHAM!

SO YOU SEE, NO SHIP COULD GET PAST HIM, AND THEREFORE NOBODY COULD GET TO AMERICA TO DISCOVER IT!

YEAH, BUT THE ANCHOR! WHAT ABOUT THE ANCHOR?

OH, THAT WAS VERY IMPORTANT! YOU SEE, COLUMBUS DECIDED TO GET RID OF MOBY MICK ONCE AND FOR ALL...

I'M GOING TO CATCH MOBY MICK!

MAP OF YE ATLANTIC

U.S.A. ←

1974

SO WHEN MOBY HIT THE SHIP A STRANGE THING HAPPENED-IT DIDN'T BUDGE AN INCH...

HOORAY! WE'RE SAFE! HE CAN'T HARM US ANY MORE!

DONG!

TUG!

WELL, THE REST'S HISTORY! COLUMBUS SAILED ON AND DISCOVERED AMERICA...

THROB!

THROB!

...AND MOBY MICK WENT OFF WITH A WHALE OF A HEADACHE!

MOAN!

YEARS TO REMEMBER

1588

ONCE a proud galleon; now a shattered hulk on the sea-bed, her drowned guns silent, her sails filling where no breeze blows.

Only days before, she had set sail, one of the one hundred and thirty fighting ships of the mighty Spanish Armada bound to invade the England of Queen Elizabeth.

But the English, under Drake and Howard, harried and chased the Dons up the east coast to the North of Scotland—and disaster.

There, scattered and battered by a wild westerly, nearly half of the Spanish ships were lost . . . and the Armada was no more. It was the year 1588.

JONAH

1653 A.D.

INTRODUCING PROFESSOR SVENSON, A SWEDISH HISTORIAN—

HA-HA! VE HAFF DONE IT!

—WHO IS A VERY HAPPY SWEDE TODAY—

—BRINGING WITH HER A DREADFUL SECRET!

COR! WHAT GOES ON? HERE'S ME QUIETLY EXPLORIN' THE OLD TUB WHEN, ALL OF A SUDDEN, UP SHE COMES!

I'D BETTER GO UP ON DECK AN' SEE WHAT'S HAPPENING!

PRINT Nº2

Verily, we know not how it came about, but some horrid clotte received ye full weight of ye cannon on his foot and, in sore distress, severed ye gun tackle.

Aghh!

Nº3

Free of its moorings, ye great cannon thundered aft~until it smote ye fiery galley chimney with ye fearfulle clang ~

Ye fiery knate

Clang

Nº4

~thus setting off ye powder.

Bang

—BUT LET US BE THANKFUL ZAT NO SUCH CREATURE EXISTS IN ZIS DAY AND AGE!

COR! THAT FUNGUS-FACED OLD FOSSIL'S GOT A PICTURE OF MY GREAT, GREAT, GREAT GRANDAD —

—THE GENIUS WHO INVENTED SQUARE CANNONBALLS THAT WOULDN'T ROLL ABOUT THE DECK IN ROUGH WEATHER—

CLATTER!

AWLK!

LOOKS AS THOUGH JONAH'S ANCESTOR HAD SOMETHING THERE—

CRUNCH!

CRAS

—FOR, AFTER FOUR YEARS OF HARD TOIL BY HIM AND HIS ASSISTANTS, A 17TH CENTURY MAN-O'-WAR HAS BEEN RAISED TO THE SURFACE.

GLUG!

HERE SHE COMES NOW—

In Sixteen Hundred and Fifty-Three The 'Prince Royal' practised gunnery. Alas, a mis-fired cannon shot Sank the ship-thanks to this clot!

MERCIFULLY UNAWARE OF THE PERIL LURKING BELOW, THE PROFESSOR PARADES A PARTY OF HIS PUPILS ON THE POOP—

GENTLEMENS! I HAFF HERE A COLLECTION OF OLD PRINTS FOUND IN THE CELLAR OF A MUSEUM—

—THEY SHOW CLEARLY HOW ZIS HISTORIC SHIP MET HER FATE IN 1653!

THANKS TO THESE PRINTS, THE PROFESSOR REVEALS A STRANGE SEA-DRAMA FROM THE DISTANT PAST—

PRINT Nº 1

In ye year of grace, 1653, ye goode shippe, "Prince Royal", was at sea when ye captain gave ye order for gunnery practice~~~

Nº 5 Up to ye yard-arm soared ye hissing shotte~

Wheeeee-e-e

Nº 6 ~ to descende with ye horrid, splintering crash ~ right through ye bottome of ye shippe~

Zounds! That hath verily torn it.

Crash

Wheee-e-e-e

Nº 7 —thus, with ye terrible glugging and ye vile blooping, did ye "Prince Royal" repair to her watery grave.

Bloop

Glugge

Now BACK TO THE PRESENT—

GENTLEMENS! TO ZIS DAY NO-ONE HASS DISCOVERED ZER TRUE IDENTITY OF ZER SHTUPID JACKASS REFERRED TO AS "YE HORRID CLOTTE"—

YE HORRID CLOTTE. 1653.

—ESPECIALLY AS THE CAPTAIN OF THE "PRINCE ROYAL" JUST LAUGHED AT THE IDEA OF SQUARE CANNONBALLS—

SHATTER! CRUMP!

—AND CALLED JONAH'S ANCESTOR "YE FANG-FACED BUFFOON"!

AND NOW, OVER TWO CENTURIES LATER, HISTORY REPEATS ITSELF!

WOW! THAT'S TORN IT!

DON'T BLAME ME, MATE! IF THAT NIT OF A CAPTAIN HAD LISTENED TO MY GREAT, GREAT GREAT GRANDPOP IN 1653, THIS WOULD NEVER HAVE HAPPENED!

AGGH-H-H! IT'S 'IM! IT'S "YE HORRID CLOTTE" —AND HE'S DONE IT AGAIN!

Jonah ye ancient mariner

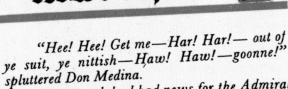

Jonah's a name we often hear —
It fills poor sailors' hearts with fear.
But if he'd lived in days of yore,
Would he have sunk tall ships galore?
Let's take him back through time and see
What kind of seaman he would be;
To be exact about the date—
It's fifteen hundred and eighty-eight . . .

One day, Sir Francis Drake was playing bowls at Plymouth Hoe while waiting to fight the Spanish Armada. Suddenly Sir Francis let out a terrible shriek. He had espied an ugly seaman with buck teeth striding towards him.

"Greetings, Sir Francis," quoth the fellow, who was, of course, Jonah. "I come to join ye Englishe fleet to help drive ye Spanish Armada from ye Channel!"

Sir Francis' beard bristled.

"Be off with ye, varlet!" he roared. "Thou art too scrawny to be a seaman on any of my ships. I need husky men, not tooth-faced, pole-bodied weaklings! If you even dare look near ye Englishe fleet, I will tie ye cannonballs to ye feet and droppe you overboard in ye deepest part of ye ocean!"

With this parting shot, Sir Francis seized the goon by the collar and the seat of his pantaloons and pitched him headlong into the Channel.

Great was Jonah's wrath as he spluttered to the surface and swam off.

"Ye rotter! Ye swabbe!" he squawked. "If you will not have me I will join ye Spaniards!"

So saying, the sea-goon headed for the distant sails of the Spanish Armada. Soon he was alongside a big galleon—the flagship of the Spanish Admiral, Don Medina.

"Heh! Heh! I spy ye open gunneport!" chuckled Jonah. "Forsooth! I will slither through it and get aboard!"

On tiptoe, Jonah sneaked through the ship until he found himself in the Admiral's cabin. Now Don Medina had broken his spectacles during a storm and he mistook Jonah for his serving lad.

"Get me into ye armour for ye coming fight with ye Englishe!" snapped Don Medina. "And stir ye lazy bones about it!"

With fumbling fingers the sea-goon did his best, but the big feather plume of Don Medina's hat became stuck down between the Admiral's back and the armour. It began to tickle right merrily!

"Hee! Hee! Get me—Har! Har!— out of ye suit, ye nittish—Haw! Haw!—goonne!" spluttered Don Medina.

But Jonah had bad news for the Admiral.. "Verily, Sire, I cannot!" spake he. "Ye strappes are stuck fast!"

Bawling with mirth and waving his arms wildly, Don Medina stumbled out on to the poop-deck, hoping that somebody there could free him.

Then the waving Admiral was spotted by look-outs on the other Spanish ships.

"Captain!" quoth one look-out. "Ye Admiral is signalling us to turn to ye starboardde—I think!"

"Signal from ye flagshippe, Captain," announced another look-out. "Turn to ye portte—I hope!"

And yet another—

"Er—Captain, Ye Admiral seems to want us to turn ye shippe about!"

And so, because of Jonah, the great Armada milled in great confusion, ships crashing into each other until many were unfit to fight.

Just then, Sir Francis Drake attacked, and you know the rest from your history books.

Suddenly, Sir Francis spotted Jonah.

"Bosun, throw a rope around ye long-faced nitte and tow him to Plymouthe," quoth Sir Francis. And that is how Jonah was brought before Good Queen Bess.

"I bidde you kneel, Jonah," ordered the Queen, borrowing a big sword from a courtier. Trembling with fear, Jonah obeyed.

"P-please, Your Majesty," he s-s-spake, " don't chop off ye bonce!"

But all the Queen did was tap the nit on the nut with the flat of the sword, saying—

"Arise, Sir Jonah! Long may you sail in ye Spanish shippes and send them to ye bottom!"

And right now if you're on a ship,
Enjoying a nice ocean trip,
You'll know that it is time to swim,
When you hear cries of—"AGHH! IT'S 'IM!"

from BEANO BOOK 1964

Minnie the Minx has "sweet dreams" when she boards a treasure ship!

Ye Bashe Streete Kyddes

The Bash Street Kids are full of fun—
They tickle readers, every one!
We wonder if such fun galore
Was had by folks in days of yore?
So let's imagine for a spell
That all the Bash Street Kids did dwell
In far-off days—say 1605,
When bold, bad Guy Fawkes was alive!

IN olden days in Merrie England, a nasty varlet by the name of Guy Fawkes decided to blow up the Houses of Parliament.

First, Guy went to look over his target.

"Yes," quoth he. "Six barrels of gunnepowder should blow this lotte off ye mappe!"

As he made his way home, a sudden clanging noise shattered the still air and a voice shouted:—

"Stand back! Ye Bashe Streete Kyddes are coming out of ye schoole."

Guy Fawkes leaped back as a horde of urchins came rushing out of the school-yard and dashed off down the King's Highway.

"Forsooth!" muttered Guy. "I wouldst not like to teach that lotte!"

Later that evening, the Bash Street Kids held a meeting on "Ye Slagge Heappe."

"Listen, varlets," said Daniel, their leader. "I'm fed up of ye school. We must get rid of it!

"Burn it to ye ground!" bellowed an ugly urchin called Plugge.

"Nay! I like school," replied a buffoon by the name of Smiffye.

"Thou art a dimme nitte!" spake Wilfridde, a strange boy with his doublet buttoned up to his nose. "I say we should blow it up."

"Good idea!" quoth Daniel. "Let us pool ye pocket money and buy ye gunnepowder."

Meanwhile, near the Houses of Parliament, Guy Fawkes had just finished digging a tunnel which led from a dingy hovel to a spot under the room where the King and the Government were to be meeting.

"Har! Har!" cackled Guy. "Their next meeting will go with ye bang, forsooth! Now I must buy ye gunnepowder."

Guy then went down to "Ye Olde Gunne-powder Shoppe," where he purchased six barrels of "Ye Beste, Bangiest Gunnepowder."

As he turned to leave, a small ragamuffin came panting in.

"How much gunnepowder can I get for one crown, two groats, three half-pence, two doublet buttons and ye dead frogge?" asked the ragamuffin, who was Smiffye, of course.

"I can give you two barrels of seconde-hande gunnepowder," replied the shop-keeper.

Vastly pleased, the urchin seized his barrels and staggered off to "Ye Slagge Heappe."

"Good manne, Smiffye!" quoth Daniel. "C'mon, kyddes! Let us go and dig ye tunnel under ye Bashe Streete Schoole."

On the night of November 5th, Guy Fawkes made his way under the Houses of Parliament.

"Heh! Heh! I'll soon blow this place sky-high!" spake Guy.

But just at that moment he trod on the Prime Minister's cat which was snoozing in the tunnel.

"YEOOOWOOYAH!" The agonised squawling of the cat brought the King's men rushing to the spot, and Guy was arrested.

He was taken before the King.

"This nasty knave was about to blow up ye Houses of Parliament, sire, but we captured him in ye nicke of tyme," said the captain of the guard.

"Well done, my stout fellows," said the King. "At least there will be no explosions today."

Hardly were the words out of his mouth than a thunderous bang rattled the Houses of Parliament and broke all the windows.

"What was that, pray?" gasped the King.

"Some urchins have just blown up ye Bashe Streete Schoole, sire," said the Prime Minister, looking through the shattered window. "I can see ye little demons dancing round ye ruins."

The Kids were dragged before the King.

"Thou wilt all write an hundred times, 'I must notte blow up ye schoole'!" bellowed the King. "And then my best swordsman will give ye sixe of ye beste with ye flatte of ye sworde!"

Now you might think these old-time Kids
Would drive a teacher mad,
But Kids at Bash Street School today
Are every bit as bad!

BOOM!

BANG!

ROAR!

BOOM!

BLAM!

BANG!

from BEANO BOOK 1964

These two Dandy lads had a history of hating each other, and got up to some rough-and-tumble that today's comics would not allow on their pages!

MR BUBBLES

Then Tim found Mr Bubbles' bottle.

AHOY THERE, TIM! WOULD YOU LIKE THREE WISHES?

WOW! MR BUBBLES! I WISH THAT PARROT WAS ALIVE AGAIN!

AWRRK!

W-W-WE'VE GONE BACK IN TIME!

WELL, THAT'S WHEN POLLY WAS ALIVE!

This weekly tale of magic from the Sparky comic always came high in readers' Popularity Polls, although it was never explained why a bubble imp should live in a plastic bottle, nor what a bubble imp actually was!

AHAR! POLLY SEEMS TO LIKE THE YOUNG 'UN! WOULD YE LIKE TO SAIL WITH ME AS CABIN BOY?

YES—I MEAN, AYE-AYE, CAP'N!

AWRRK!

Tim was busy when the ship sailed—

HERE'S YOUR DINNER, CAP'N!

GOOD LAD! NOW TAKE POLLY AND GIVE 'ER SOME GRUB TOO!

OH, NO! WE'VE BEEN HIT! I WISH THE SHIP WAS WHOLE AGAIN!

SECOND WISH, TIM!

AHAR! PREPARE TO BOARD!

B-BUT WE HOLED THE PIRATE SHIP! SHE SHOULD BE SINKING!

ALONG THE PLANK WITH YE, DOG!

THAT'S MY ANCESTOR ON THE PLANK! I WISH I'D NEVER STARTED THIS!

LAST WISH, TIM!

Back home—

DON'T TOUCH THE PARROT, TIM! THEY SAY HE BELONGED TO A PIRATE!

I KNOW THE STORY'S TRUE!

TA-RA!

Royal Parade

Elizabeth

ELIZABETH I, 1558–1603

THE Golden Age of Good Queen Bess — in these glowing words historians have described the reign of Elizabeth I. It was indeed a time of great prosperity. Things like carpets, tea, potatoes and watches were introduced to the country. Much better houses were built and for the first time glass was used for making windows. Towns grew in size, and London became the most important trading city in the world.

Much of England's greatness was due to her courageous seamen. Men like Hawkins, Gilbert, Raleigh and Drake, made many voyages of exploration and opened up new trade routes. Then in 1588 Drake crushed the Spanish Armada, and in so doing gave England command of the seas.

Elizabeth died in 1603 after one of the longest reigns in history—a reign in which she had helped her country become the most powerful nation of the age.

William Shakespeare, the great English playwright, lived in Elizabeth's time, and many of his plays were performed before the Queen.

In 1583 Sir Humphrey Gilbert, with Elizabeth's approval, landed in Newfoundland and founded the first British colony.

The first coach was made in England in 1564. The picture shows an early State Coach.

FROM THE BEEZER BOOK 1964

WW
Wuzzy Wiz, a magician from The Dandy of fifty years ago, found he had to pull his "stocks" up when he went on a journey through time!
WW

THAT'S WHEN A DARING CHAP LIKE ME SHOULD HAVE LIVED~IN THE EXCITING DAYS OF GOOD QUEEN BESS. I KNOW~I'LL GET MY MAGIC WAND TO TAKE ME BACK. LET'S SEE WHERE I LAND.

OLDEN STOCKS

GOOD QUEEN BESS

WHIZZ

ODDS SOCKS! SOMETHING HAS GONE WRONG~AND HERE COME PEASANTS TO PELT ME. SAVE ME, MAGIC WAND.

OOH! STOP IT SOMEBODY!

SHIP'S CARPENTER
TAR MERCHANT

WOW! STRAIGHT FOR THAT TAR TUB!

TAR

CARPENTER
FRONT ENTRANCE
ROUND CORNER

GROOGH! YES, IT'S ME~ WUZZY.

TARRED AND NOW FEATHERED, EGAD!

OUCH! I'VE CRASHED ~BUT I'M FREE OF THE STOCKS ANYWAY.

WE ONLY WANT TO RETURN THE STICK YOU DROPPED, SIR!

YEARS TO REMEMBER

1666

The Great Fire of London that destroyed many square miles of the old city, brought an unexpected benefit. On the sites cleared by the flames rose many of the important and beautiful buildings that exist today.

But the fleeing Londoners had no such thoughts in their minds. For it was 1666, and London was burning . . .

FROM THE SPARKY BOOK 1972

JIMMY AND HIS MAGIC PATCH

In modern times, safety precautions are of primary concern, so this Magic Patch story shows how different life was in the 1940s! Stirrup pumps, rationing coupons, children building bonfires — with the help of dangerous flammable liquid! Even Jimmy's exhortation in the second caption would not be looked upon with favour nowadays!

1 — Jimmy Watson was spending Saturday afternoon clearing up the tool-shed in his father's garden. The bonfire he had made with the rubbish was blazing away merrily for Jimmy had made sure the junk would light by adding some paraffin. Jimmy was pleased with his job but he was also feeling like some adventure after the hard work. As he stood there with the tin of paraffin in one hand and an old stirrup pump in the other a fire engine dashed by on its way to a fire.

2 — "Just the job," breathed Jimmy. "What wouldn't I give to see a real stunning blaze!" Whizz! In a couple of winks Jimmy had left the Watson garden and was on his way through time. For Jimmy's pants were patched with a very special patch which could whisk him back magically to any time in history. And now Jimmy was being whisked back to the Great Fire of London 'way back in 1666. As Jimmy landed, the buildings were crashing everywhere in flames.

3 — Jimmy hadn't been on the spot long enough to gasp when a big burly citizen wrenched the paraffin tin from the young lad's grasp. "Water!" he cried. "I must have water to save my house." "Hey! Don't use that!" said Jimmy. "Stand clear," roared the big fellow and hurled the contents of the paraffin tin.

4 — Swoosh! As the paraffin hit the flames they blazed up more fiercely than ever, while the fellow gaped in terror, for paraffin was unknown in those days. "That's done it," gulped Jimmy. "Now I'll have to help him to put out the fire." Quickly Jim sank the barrel of the stirrup pump in a ditch beside the house.

5 — Jimmy was just getting busy with the pump when he was interrupted. "Arrest that boy," shrieked a woman nearby. "He's a fire-raiser. He was carrying some fire-raising chemicals in his tin." It was the wife of the house-owner and with her were two soldiers, who levelled their muskets, for no mercy was shown to suspicious persons during the Great Fire of London!

6 — But Jimmy Watson fired first. The powerful spray from the stirrup pump caught the first guard clean between the eyes and, while the second soldier paused in amazement, Jimmy Watson turned and darted off with his stirrup pump through the nearest gate-way. "Even King Charles himself wouldn't keep me here any longer than I can help," he panted, as he ran.

7 — Then Jimmy's heart thumped with horror as he dashed through the gate-way. He was in the courtyard of a house and his scape was blocked by a twelve-foot wall. Behind him clattered he soldiers convinced by now that Jimmy had started the Fire of London and was secretly assisting the spread of the fire. Whirling the barrel of the stirrup pump like a lasso, Jimmy made it catch between two of the projections on the wall.

8 — Then Jimmy scrambled up the rubber hose. As he tumbled over the wall a coach came flying round the corner in flames. The horses were bolting in terror from the flames. It was the Royal Coach with the King in it, and Jimmy was so amazed that he dropped off the wall and into the moat. Luckily for Jimmy the house behind was now on fire and the soldiers had turned to fight the blaze, so he had a few minutes to spare.

9 — Once more Jimmy got busy with the pump in an effort to stop the mad gallop of the horses. He aimed the first jet of water at the horses' heads and brought them up in their tracks right away. King Charles jumped out of the coach. "Good work, lad," he bellowed. "Now I'll give you a hand to save the coach." Jimmy had made a friend at last.

10 — The tapestry and velvet of the coach was blazing away merrily. "Golly. That stuff must have cost a lot of coupons!" gasped Jimmy as he worked at the pump handle. "But Charlie here knows how to use the stirrup pump. We'll soon have everything under control." Sure enough! The King aimed skilful jets and the flames were successfully put out.

11 — Jimmy and the King did not stop there, however. A nearby butcher's shop had caught fire and the two-man fire brigade got busy on that too. This time King Charles did the heavy work with the pump while Jimmy played the water on the blaze. The butcher stood by bellowing advice, but Jimmy knew his stuff. Soon the flames were beaten and the shop was saved.

12 — U-m-m! Jimmy licked his lips. The tasty smell of roasting joints had given him an appetite. "Are you hungry, boy?" roared Charles. "You shall eat what you want. Attend to him, butcher!" And King Charles rode off while Jimmy sat down to feed. But he had just finished the last drop of gravy when — bonk! — he was whisked back to modern times again.

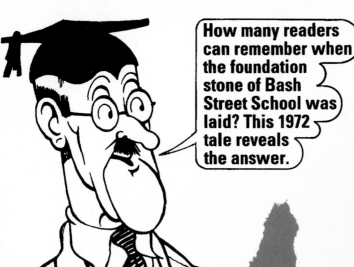

How many readers can remember when the foundation stone of Bash Street School was laid? This 1972 tale reveals the answer.

YOU'RE GETTING A NEW CLASSROOM. COME WITH ME.

PLUG

IN THESE DAYS, THE SCHOOL WAS LIT BY CANDLES.

COME OUT, THE KNAVE WHO BLEW OUT MY CANDLE!

THEN A FOOLISH FAT URCHIN ATE ALL THE CANDLES!

HMPH! PRETTY TASTELESS ROCK THIS! — CHOMP!

LATER, THE SCHOOL HAD PARAFFIN LAMPS, BUT THE CHILDREN WERE ALWAYS BREAKING THE WINDOWS AND THE WIND BLEW THE LAMPS OUT!

ICY BLAST

PHUT!

THAT'S THE REASON FOR THE NEW CLASSROOM! OUR MOTTO AT BASH ST. IS "PROGRESS, ALWAYS PROGRESS!"

WILFRID

DINNER TIME —

DING! DING! DING!

REPORT TO YOUR NEW CLASSROOM AT TWO O'CLOCK

THUNDER!

AFTER DINNER —

THIS ROOM IS A GREAT IMPROVEME H'M! THAT FOOLISH BOY, SMIFFY, IS LATE AS USUAL.

KID-PROOF

REGISTER

AN HOUR LATER —

HO!! SMIFFY, HAVE YOU FORGOTTEN ABOUT THE NEW CLASSROOM?

CRUMBS! I KNEW THERE WAS SOMETHING.

I'D BETTER RUN, OR I'LL BE LATE.

JANITOR'S CAT

SO —

HELLO, TEACHER! I FOUND THIS POLE!

"THE NEW CLASS IIB

WILD YOUNG DIRKY

The spy-hunt through the streets of Perth.

THE town of Perth was crowded with men of Prince Charlie's army, taking part in the great Rebellion against King George. It was early in the year 1746, and the Highlanders had halted their northward retreat to wait for stragglers. The stay in Perth also provided an opportunity to attend to weapons in need of repair, and Highland armourers had commandeered several forges in the town. In one smithy, Rory MacLean and Fat Duncan Stewart, both expert blacksmiths, were hard at work. Wild Young Dirky was their assistant, working the bellows when required. But now Dirky was leaning in the doorway, watching the bustle in the street.

2—"Duncan!" said Dirky suddenly. "Here's that French soldier we noticed this morning—and the cripple beggar's there again!" Duncan joined Dirky in the doorway. On the far side of the street, a beggar sat with his back against a wall; strutting jauntily towards him came a soldier in the uniform of the French troops serving with the Highland army. As he drew abreast of the beggar, the Frenchman put a hand into a pocket of his coat, tossed the cripple what looked like a coin wrapped in a scrap of paper, and strode briskly on. "That's three times now we've seen him throw money to the beggar," said Dirky excitedly.

3—Duncan nodded grimly. "Aye, lad, there's something queer afoot here," he growled. "We'll just keep an eye on Mr Johnnie Frenchman." After a word to Rory, the two set out to follow the dapper little soldier. Before long, the Frenchman approached a group of officers serving in Ogilvy's Regiment, and began conversation. Dirky and Duncan, hovering nearby, heard most of it, and exchanged meaning looks as the Frenchman, leaving Ogilvy's

4—Dirky and Duncan, keeping at a distance, followed the Frenchman into a neighbouring street. At the door of a tavern stood several clansmen of Gordon's Regiment; and at once the Frenchman strolled up to them. Dirky and Duncan got near enough to overhear his chatter. After a time, the Frenchman entered the tavern. But it was not long before he emerged, and made for the street where the cripple beggar sat. And as he passed the cripple, the Frenchman tossed him a coin wrapped in paper.

These pages are from The Topper 1959

6—The haft of the dirk struck the beggar's head, and he pitched face-foremost on the cobbles. Yet despite the blow, and the force of his fall, he was scrambling to his feet when Dirky leapt astride his back and sent him sprawling once more. The lad forced the blade of a dirk between the beggar's teeth, and levered his jaws apart. The man choked, and the ball of paper fell from his mouth just as Rory MacLean, who had seen the chase from the smiddy, came running up.

5—"Now, Dirky!" shouted Fat Duncan, and, leaping suddenly forward, he tackled the Frenchman. But the "cripple" beggar was too quick for Dirky; he leapt to his feet, seized his crutch, and was away like the wind. As he ran, the man crumpled up the paper in which the coin had been wrapped, and stuffed it into his mouth with the obvious intention of swallowing it. Dirky, racing in pursuit, saw this action and, without so much as checking in his stride, drew a dirk and hurled it.

7—Dirky speared the paper and offered it to Rory. "This beggar's a spy!" he cried. "Aye," growled Fat Duncan, striding up with the little Frenchman in his grasp. "And this little French toad is mixed up in his rotten game." Rory gave a low whistle of surprise as he scanned what was written upon the paper—information about the Highland army, of great value to the Redcoats. "Aye, Dirky," said Rory softly. "You and Duncan have laid hands on two spies, sure enough!" By this time a crowd had gathered. Among the onlookers were men of Ogilvy's Regiment, and Rory asked them to march the prisoners to their commander's headquarters.

8—In Ogilvy's headquarters, Dirky and Duncan told how they overheard the Frenchman ferreting out information from men of various regiments. Meantime, it was discovered that the shoulder-rest of the beggar's crutch was hollow; in this hiding-place were found notes similar to that which Dirky had prevented the man from swallowing. The fate of the Frenchman and the beggar was sealed; they were spies in the pay of the Redcoats, and they were marched off to be shot for their treachery.

WILD YOUNG DIRKY

Duncan plays the fool—to fool the Redcoats!

"PATIENCE, lads. You'll taste the air o' freedom yet!" growled Fat Duncan Stewart, crouched in the back door of the Sidlaw Tavern, in Perth. The big Highlander's eyes were watching an army waggon which had just rumbled into the town. Chained to a pole sticking from the rear of it were six limping, wounded Highlanders, captured by King George's Redcoats during the northward retreat of Prince Charlie's army, early in the year 1746. Along with Wild Young Dirky, Duncan had been left in Perth to find out the strength of the Redcoats. Over the past few days, they had done this.

2—"Fergie!" Fat Duncan turned to call the innkeeper, while Dirky remained by the hotel, watching the manacled Highlanders. The little, shaggy-haired innkeeper came running. "You are leaving, then, Duncan?" he asked. "Aye," answered the big man grimly. "Our boat is ready do___ by the river bank; but we've a little job to do before we go. Is that fat H___ ___ ___" For answer, Fergie threw open the door of the front parlour. ___ ___ ___ ___ ___ ___ sprawled a hefty Hessian soldier, one of the many ___ ___ s. Fat Duncan smiled. "Leave us," he said softly.

3—Outside, Dirky heard a scuffle in the inn parlour. A few minutes later, he gaped as Fat Duncan, resplendent in the frocked tunic and top-boots of the Hessian, swaggered forth. "I am going to distract the attention of the Redcoats," Duncan chuckled, "with the aid of Fergie's ale. But I depend on you to get word to these prisoners." Dirky hastily scribbled a note on a scrap of paper. This he speared with one of his dirks. Shortly after, Fat Duncan swaggered out to the Redcoat waggon.

___ ___ ___ ___ ___ ___ his companion reach the waggon and begin to parley with the ___coats. Then he took careful aim at the beam behind the waggon, and hurled the dirk bearing the message. Fat Duncan, armed with tankards of ale, and jabbering a strange mumbo-jumbo which he hoped would be taken for German, kept the Redcoats entertained. None of the thirsty troops heard the thud as the dirk embedded itself in the beam holding the prisoners. But Dirky's message was read, and the six men were ready.

5—By now, Fat Duncan was warming to his work. Staggering a little, and slopping ale from his tankard, he suddenly drew his sword. "Hessian—goot swordsman—" he bellowed, and pranced forward. Dirky pulled a lever close at hand. Two halves of a trap-door in the floor suddenly fell away behind Duncan, disclosing the innkeeper's cellar beneath. The Redcoats roared applause. But their laughter changed to cries of alarm as Duncan suddenly pranced to the rear of the cart and, with one mighty stroke, cleft the pole holding the Highlanders. Then the fat impostor blundered about, hindering the troopers.

6—The Highlanders, forewarned by Dirky's note, were free of the pole in a trice, and running for the door of the nearby inn. Then Fat Duncan, pretending to realise what harm he had done, gave a bellow of rage and lumbered in pursuit, still brandishing his naked sword. The Redcoat guard commander was livid with rage. "That Hessian pig!" he roared. "He'll cost us our heads. After them! And take the Hessian as well!" But the escaping prisoners were by now tumbling through the door of the inn.

7—Inside the tavern, Dirky was standing at one side of the open door as the freed Highlanders rushed in. "Turn left," he cried. "Out the side door and to the river. A boat waits!" Next moment, Fat Duncan loomed in the doorway. "Right, Dirky!" he roared, and sprang forward. Dirky pulled a lever close at hand. Two halves of a trap-door in the floor suddenly fell away behind Duncan, disclosing the innkeeper's cellar beneath. The leading pair of Redcoats, pell-mell on Duncan's heels, tumbled headlong down among the barrels of ale, and the others jammed in the doorway.

8—Duncan's scheme had worked faultlessly. He and Dirky were hard on the prisoners' heels as they reached the waters of the Tay nearby, and launched the waiting boat. The Highlanders bent to the oars, and the boat shot out into the current. Just then the first of the pursuing troopers burst from the Sidlaw Tavern, and a few musket balls raised splashes in the water alongside. But powerful strokes took the row-boat to safety. Later that day, Dirky and Duncan led six happy Highlandmen over the hills beyond Perth—on their way to join the Highland army on its march north.

Along with the serious side of Scottish life in the 18th century, the comics showed that kilted Highlanders could raise a laugh. One such (ever-hungry) Highlander was . . .

The Beano's McTickle family from the early '70s took 'Scottishness' to its silliest extremes, with a porridge swamp for starters(!) and an amazing animal known as the Orang-McHaggis which zoologists have yet to track down (outside the pages of The Beano, that is!)

In 1801, the Union Flag, or Union Jack as it is often known, came into being. In 1978, The Beano's Ball Boy fell foul of that very flag!

1978

WE'RE PLAYING A SCHOOLS' CUP FINAL IN THIS STADIUM TODAY, READERS—I'M HOPING TO HAVE A GREAT GAME!

During the game—

WHAT A RUN DOWN THE WING!

OUT!

NO, IT WASN'T!

IT WAS! OOPS —SORRY!

BOK!

PESKY FLAG!

Later—

NOW FOR ONE OF MY CURLING CORNER KICKS!

PLUP!

GLUMPH!

SOPPY SHOT

SNARL! MORE FLAG TROUBLE! THE 'KEEPER SAVED THAT SHOT EASILY!

But—

SORRY—THE ROPE BROKE!

RAGE!

Later—

ONLY THE GOALIE TO BEAT—THIS MUST BE THE WINNER!

PLUP!

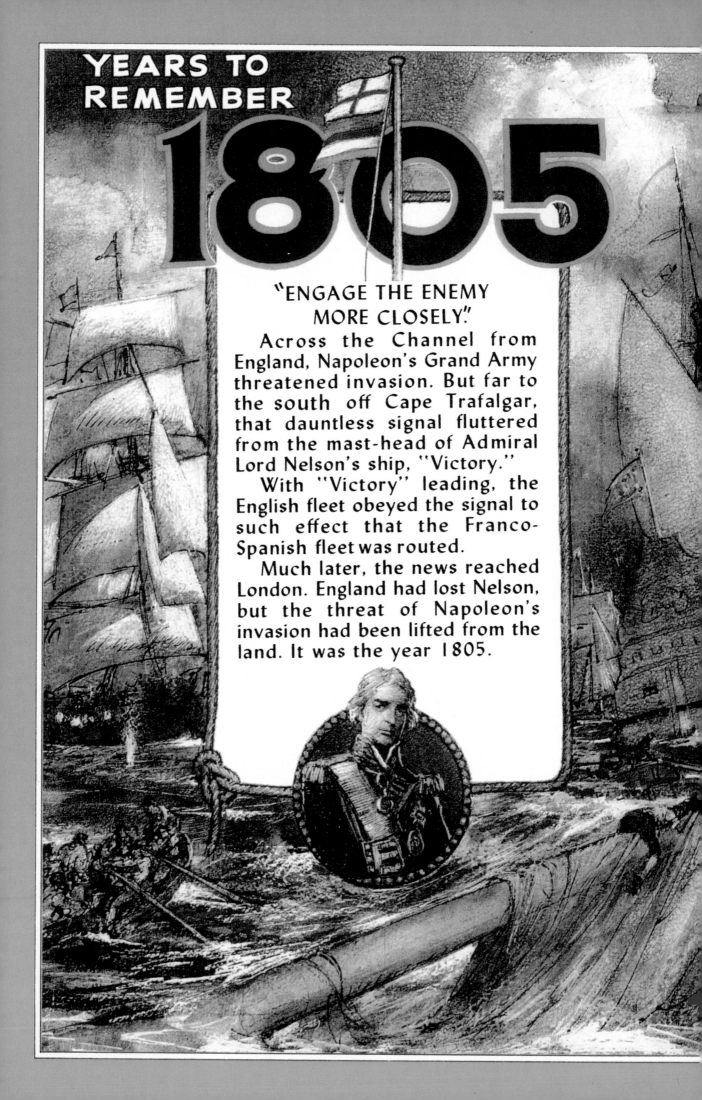

YEARS TO REMEMBER

1805

"ENGAGE THE ENEMY MORE CLOSELY."

Across the Channel from England, Napoleon's Grand Army threatened invasion. But far to the south off Cape Trafalgar, that dauntless signal fluttered from the mast-head of Admiral Lord Nelson's ship, "Victory."

With "Victory" leading, the English fleet obeyed the signal to such effect that the Franco-Spanish fleet was routed.

Much later, the news reached London. England had lost Nelson, but the threat of Napoleon's invasion had been lifted from the land. It was the year 1805.

FROM THE
SPARKY BOOK 1972

NAPOLEON BONAPARTE

How did a poor Corsican youth, small of stature and thin, rise to become a giant figure whose shadow fell across the whole of Europe — the famous Emperor Napoleon? At a time when almost every European country was at war — when kingdoms were tumbling and revolution had France in its grip — the young Bonaparte chose to be a soldier. And it was in the art of war that he became a giant. Under his command the French Armies seemed to be invincible, and all Europe trembled at the sound of his name. It took a thousand battles and a score of wars before the giant met his defeat at Waterloo. The little Corsican's name is one of the few that will never be forgotten.

123 years after the real battle (and 36 years before the song made famous by ABBA) Korky tried to pinch some sausages, but the Army soon "got shot of him", and Korky met his own Waterloo! And he didn't seem to notice what the cook is putting in the Army stew!

Roger THE OLD-TIME Dodger

Our Roger is a cunning boy,
For dodging is his greatest joy.
Except for Dad, there are but few
Whom crafty Roger can't outdo . . .
Now, just for fun, we'll make him soar
Through time and space to days of yore.
What dodges would be on his list
For folks like famous Oliver Twist?

ONE day, Roger was strolling through the streets of Old London when he espied a little boy looking in at the window of a pie-shop.

"Good day, young fellow!" chirped Roger. "And what may your name be?"

"I am Oliver Twist," quoth the lad, "and I am going to buy a juicy pie with my last penny. 'Tis a lucky penny, for, see, it has a hole in it. But I want that pie."

"Oho!" thought Roger. "He has exactly one penny more than I do. In that case I must twist Master Twist. I'll use Dodge No. 3."

He smiled sweetly at Oliver.

"Listen, Oliver," he said. "I'll wager you one penny that I can obtain a juicy pie from that shop without paying."

"Er—all right, then," Oliver gulped.

Roger held out his hand.

"Lend me your penny first," he chuckled. "Don't worry—you'll get it back."

Oliver handed over the coin and a few seconds later he watched Roger amble into the pie-shop.

Suddenly Oliver gasped. The pieman gave Roger a pie all right — but Oliver saw the boy hand over his penny!

As Roger strolled out of the shop, munching loudly, Oliver shook a little fist in his face.

"You spent my penny, you rogue!" he cried.

"Calm yourself—munch!—friend," chuckled Roger. "I said—chomp!—you would—chew!— get your—munch!—penny back. Here it—chew! —comes now."

So saying Roger began to wind in a long piece of thread which he had tied to the penny. Immediately, the coin was dragged from the pieman's pocket, out of the shop and into Roger's hand!

"Here is your penny, Oliver," grinned Roger. "But I won our wager, so I'll just keep it."

With that, Roger strolled away down the street, chuckling merrily to himself.

But Roger's mirth suddenly ended.

"Stop that boy! He's picked my pocket!"

Roger's hair stood to attention. It was the pieman! Oliver Twist must have spilled the beans. And two policemen were with the pieman.

Roger took to his heels and fairly bounded away. After him pounded the three men.

The boy had scurried along a couple of streets when a soft voice stopped him in his tracks.

"Psst! Come here a minute!"

Roger looked into a dark alleyway in which stood an urchin wearing a long, ragged coat and a big hat.

"You on the run from the police, friend?" asked the urchin.

Roger nodded quickly, and at once the other boy took off his coat and hat.

"Wear these, friend!" he said. "They'll disguise you from the police."

Roger's face brightened.

"A fine dodge, fellow!" he chuckled, putting on the coat and hat. "Thank you."

But the urchin had not waited for thanks.

Roger shrugged his shoulders and sauntered out into the street as the pieman and the police came puffing along.

"Good day, gentlemen!" he smiled, bowing low. "Lovely day for a run."

Then he straightened up with a jerk as the pieman seized him in a grip of iron.

"The pie thief!" he panted to the policeman. "A young villain wearing this coat stole a dozen pies from my shop this morning!"

Roger's mouth gaped like a cave. And it wasn't until he was released from prison a month later that he learned that the cunning urchin who had dodgered him was the Artful Dodger himself!

No, Roger wouldn't change his ways
If he lived in the good old days . . .
So watch your step if YOU should meet
The Dodger coming down the street!

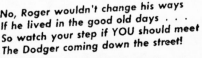

During the 1940s and 1950s, Jimmy's Magic Patch transported him to many amazing places, including Delhi at the time of the Indian Mutiny of the 1850s.

DUDLEY WATKINS

1946

ROYAL PARADE

Victoria R

VICTORIA
1837 ~ 1901

QUEEN VICTORIA came to the throne at the age of 18, a mere girl, yet she was to steer her country through troublous times.

There were riots in England and Ireland, wars in India, Abyssinia, the Sudan, the Crimea and South Africa, but in spite of all the trouble abroad great progress was made at home in science, literature and political reform.

For it was an age of great men as well as a great Queen. Palmerston, Disraeli and Gladstone in politics, Tennyson, Wordsworth and Dickens in literature, and Faraday and Darwin in science, all played their part in making the reign of Queen Victoria the most glorious in English history.

The fi
stamps were u
The illustrat
"Penny Black"
specimens of
worth about £

The Flying Scotsman made its firs
run from London to Edinburgh in 1862
The picture shows a "Stirling" locomotiv
of 1870. This can still be seen in Yor
railway museum.

The Charge of the Light Brigade.

...esive postage ...Victoria's reign. ...ws the famous ...40. Unused ...mp are now

In 1838 "The Sirius" made history. It was the first British steamship to cross the Atlantic powered by steam.

FROM THE
BEEZER BOOK 1964

THE GIANTS

It was in June 1940 that a giant arose in England. With his army driven from Dunkirk, and leader of a defenceless nation, he faced the armed might of the German Reich across the narrow English Channel, and thundered, "We shall fight on the beaches . . . in the streets . . . in the hills . . . we shall never surrender."
In courage and determination he towered over ordinary men, and inspired his country to withstand the air onslaught and naval siege that followed.
He was the "giant" called CHURCHILL.

SIR WINSTON CHURCHILL

Lord Snooty (or Lord Marmaduke of Bunkerton, to give him his full title) was eager to 'do his bit' for the war effort in 1941, as these two anti-Hitler pages demonstrate!

Dreamy Daniel, from Sparky comic of the '70s, was thirty years late with his version of the Resistance fighters in France during the Second World War — and, nearly thirty years later, there's still no resisting the laughs!

The Second World War had all but ended when this little bit of Dandy history was published. October 1945 was when Desperate Dan first met his little nephew, Danny. The world was at peace, but poor Dan wasn't, thanks to Danny's antics!

SIGNS OF THE TIMES

1. Before tarred roads were the norm, stone cobbled streets had to be washed down on a regular basis, due to the build-up of dust and dirt. Horse-drawn water sprayers were the most efficient method.

2. Slightly stronger than Biffo's tent were the "instant" houses of the '40s, called prefabs — short for "prefabricated" — (supposedly) temporary dwellings made from pre-built wall and roof sections. Built to last for five to ten years, there are still some in use in modern times.

3. Prams were very sturdy constructions in the '40s. Let's hope Biffo's borrowed tailor's dummy is, too, because it looks like there's going to be an accident!

4. A common sight on popu... beaches sixty years ago was... "Punch and Judy Man," with... tiny theatre and hand-puppets.

5. Biffo's iron probably would ha... been either heated on a fire or h... boiling hot water inside it, where... it's much easier nowadays w... electric irons that have 3-positi... variable steam spray, non-st... sole-plate, anti-scale system . . . . you still have to guide it with y... own arm!

6. Think of today's bicycles w... suspension, low-profile forks, ... gears, v-brakes and aerodynam... frame. Now look at Biffo's 19... bike!

2

3

5

4

-BUT THERE'S NO SIGN OF THEM NOW!

Biffo the Bear of the 1940s was full of ordinary everyday objects which have either disappeared completely or have altered almost beyond recognition.

7. This chap would stop anywhere to sell from his cycle-propelled ice-cream store. It must've been a tiring job, so how much of his own ice-cream did he eat?!

8. A good big solid cooker was what was wanted sixty years ago, with visible gas supply at the rear! Thank goodness for today's eye-level grills and microwave ovens!

9. Biffo's vacuum cleaner looks quite different from the models of today — *and* he didn't have a choice of bagged or bagless, vortex or cyclone, edge-cleaning, self-adjusting head, carpet or hard floor, stair-cleaning hose, filtered, wet pick-up, drain unblocker...!

10. Fireplaces such as the one in Biffo's house where the sheep are warming themselves(!) were enormous constructions with coal fires for heating and cooking, usually with an oven to one side of the fire grate.

7

8

9

10

6

In 1959 Bash Street became Milky Way, "tankers" to the kids' thirst-driven efforts to get their regular supply of school milk — which in those days was provided free to all children in primary and secondary schools.

Corporal Clott, from The Dandy, didn't quite ape the success of Hillary and Tensing, but his Mountain Rescue Team really made a monkey out of him!

Everest, the world's highest mountain, was finally conquered when Edmund P. Hillary and Sherpa Tenzing reached the summit on May 29, 1953.

I AM RUNNING A CLIMBING COMPETITION TO FIND OUT WHICH IS THE BEST TEAM. THE WINNERS WILL BECOME THE MOUNTAIN RESCUE SQUAD!

WELL, I'M BLOWED! LOOK AT CLOTT'S TEAM—A TEAM OF DRESSED-UP MONKEYS.

WE'RE OFF! THESE MONKEYS ARE TERRIFIC CLIMBERS, SIR! WE'LL RESCUE THE CRASHED AIRMEN!

OOYAH!

WHILE CLOTT LIES DAZED HIS TEAM-MATES SCOFF ALL THE BANANAS.

CLOTT WAKES UP

GUZZLING GORILLAS! THE BRUTES HAVE EATEN THE LOT! WHAT DO I DO NOW?

I'LL FOOL THEM! I'LL STUFF THIS BANANA SKIN WITH MOSS!

PRESENTLY, AFTER THE MONKEYS HAVE LEFT—

HELLO, THERE, SOLDIER! WE'RE THE CRASHED AIRMEN!

OH, GOOD! I'VE COME TO RESCUE YOU!

WE DON'T NEED RESCUING! WE'VE GOT PARACHUTES! CHEERIO!

HEY! WHAT ABOUT ME? I NEED RESCUED NOW!

WE'LL DROP IN ON YOUR COLONEL AND TELL HIM! SO LONG!

THE TEAMS START THE CLIMB

THAT'S A SCRUFFY MOB CLOTT'S GOT WITH HIM! WONDER WHO THEY ARE?

SUFFERING SERGEANTS! CLOTT'S WON! HE'S FIRST AT THE TOP!

PRESENTLY

SIR! SIR! AN AEROPLANE HAS CRASHED IN THE MOUNTAINS!

HEAR THAT, CLOTT? WELL, YOU AND YOUR TEAM ARE THE MOUNTAIN RESCUE SQUAD—OFF YOU GO!

RIGHT, SIR! I'LL ROUND MY SQUAD UP!

ON THE MOUNTAIN

AS LONG AS I KEEP TOSSING BANANAS AHEAD. THEY KEEP PULLING ME UP!

BUT THEN ONE BANANA GOES ASTRAY—

HEY, STOP! DON'T JUMP ACROSS THIS GORGE!

THERE YOU ARE, YOU CHEEKY CHIMPS! HEE-HEE! THAT'S DONE THE TRICK!

BUT THE MONKEYS ARE WILD NOW!

HELP!

AND THIS IS HOW WILD THEY ARE!

LATER

OH, GOODY! THEY HAVEN'T FORGOTTEN ABOUT ME! HOPE THERE'S A PARACHUTE INSIDE THIS PARCEL!

CLOTT

OH, NO!

Dear Clott,
Glad to hear you're on top of the world. Take a year's leave and stay there. Best Wishes The Colonel

NICK KELLY, SPECIAL AGENT, IS ON THE TRACK OF A GANG OF BANK ROBBERS WHO USE LAUGHING GAS TO HELP THEM IN THEIR RAIDS. A BROKEN GLASS TUBE IS THE ONLY CLUE THAT KELLY HAS. IT WAS LEFT BY THE CROOKS AT A BANK THEY RAIDED......

WE'LL TAKE ROVER WITH US, CEDRIC, AND SEARCH THE WEST END OF THE TOWN WHERE ALL THE CROOKS HANG OUT!

HERE WE ARE, CEDRIC! FROM HERE ON WE GO ON FOOT!

THIS BROKEN GLASS TUBE IS ALL WE HAVE TO GO ON. SNIFF IT, ROVER. SEE IF YOU CAN GET THE SCENT OF THE CROOKS.

ROVER'S LAUGHING! GOSH! I FORGOT THERE ARE STILL TRACES OF LAUGHING GAS IN THE TUBE.

IN A NEARBY HOUSE THE BANDITS ARE COUNTING THEIR LOOT.

WHAT'S THAT NOISE? I'LL TAKE A LOOK!

WHAT ARE WE GOING TO DO WITH ROVER, CEDRIC? HE'S WEAK WITH LAUGHTER.

IT-IT'S NICK KELLY! HE MUST BE HOT ON OUR TRAIL!

KELLY! QUICK—HIDE THE MONEY!

WE'RE NOT BEATEN YET! GIVE ME A TUBE OF THE LAUGHING GAS!

I'LL SLIP IT UNDER THE MAT IN HIS CAR!

WE'LL HAVE TO ABANDON OUR SEARCH UNTIL ROVER GETS OVER THE GIGGLES!

STUPID DOG!

Nick Kelly, Special Agent, from The Topper comic in the 1960s, never got himself in a lather — despite owning an icon of the '60s, a bubble car!

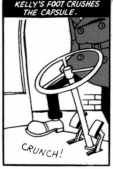

KELLY'S FOOT CRUSHES THE CAPSULE.

CRUNCH!

CEDRIC, I CAN -SNIFF- SMELL SOMETHING -SNIFF- THAT SMELLS LIKE.....

..., OH, NO! HO-HO-HO!... NOT LAUGHING GAS...HO-HO! WE'VE BEEN .... HO-HO!..CAUGHT!

KELLY IS TOO WEAK TO CONTROL THE CAR PROPERLY....

HELP!

KEEP OUR ROADS SAFE

I SUPPOSE YOU THINK THAT'S FUNNY, EH?

HO-HO!

I'M GOING TO.... SNIFF ...HO-HO! HEE-HEE!...

....RUN YOU LOT IN FOR DANGEROUS DRIVING!.... HO-HO-HO!

YOU CAN'T ...HO-HO!.. OFFICER... HA-HA!

1963

Forget all the old Indian ways — no more tracking, smoke signals or hunting! So says The Beano's Little Plum, who has hauled his fellow braves into modern times by bringing a new meaning to the phrase "attacking your food"!

YEARS TO REMEMBER
1969

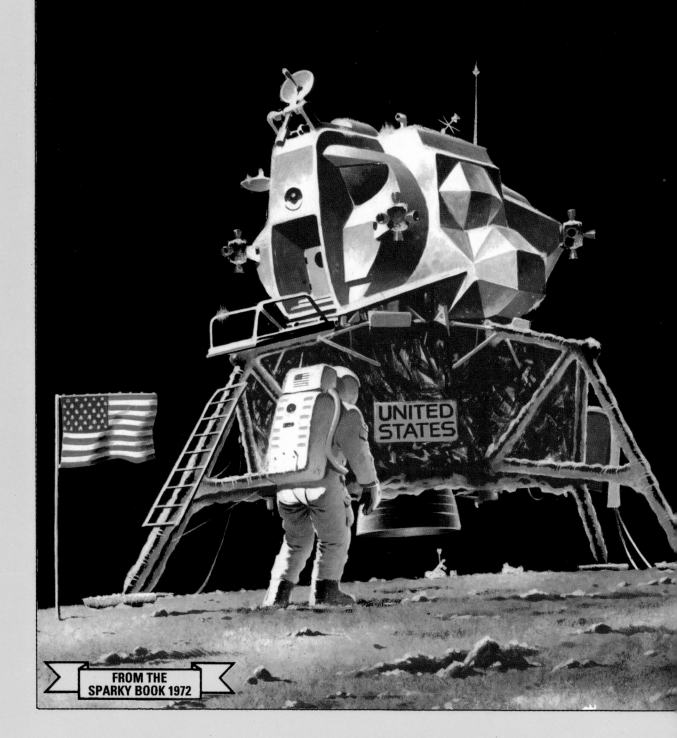

UNITED STATES

FROM THE
SPARKY BOOK 1972

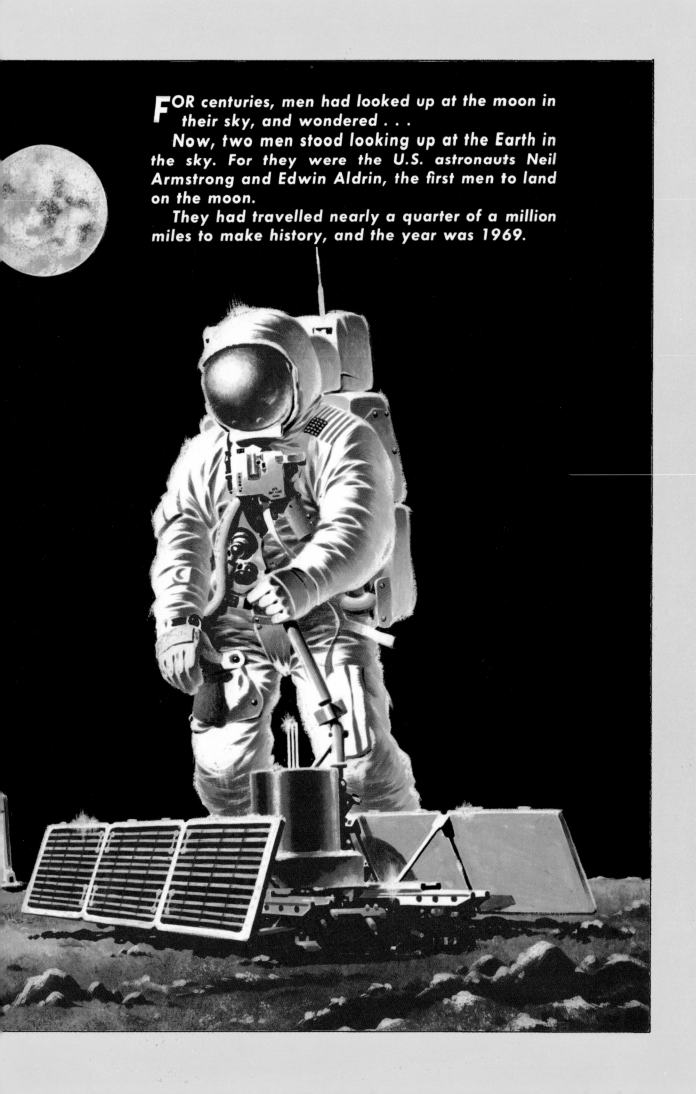

FOR centuries, men had looked up at the moon in their sky, and wondered . . .

Now, two men stood looking up at the Earth in the sky. For they were the U.S. astronauts Neil Armstrong and Edwin Aldrin, the first men to land on the moon.

They had travelled nearly a quarter of a million miles to make history, and the year was 1969.

1941

Psst! Don't tell Armstrong and Aldrin, who thought they were the first men on the moon back in 1969, but Desperate Dan reached there 28 years previously, back in 1941 without a space-ship! It all started when Dan was made sheriff of the town the previous week...

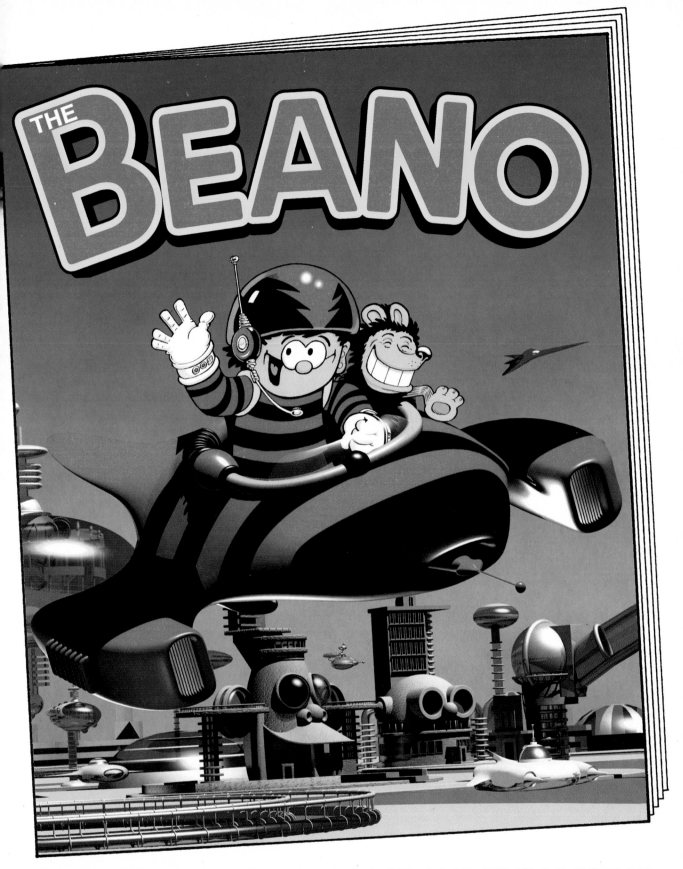

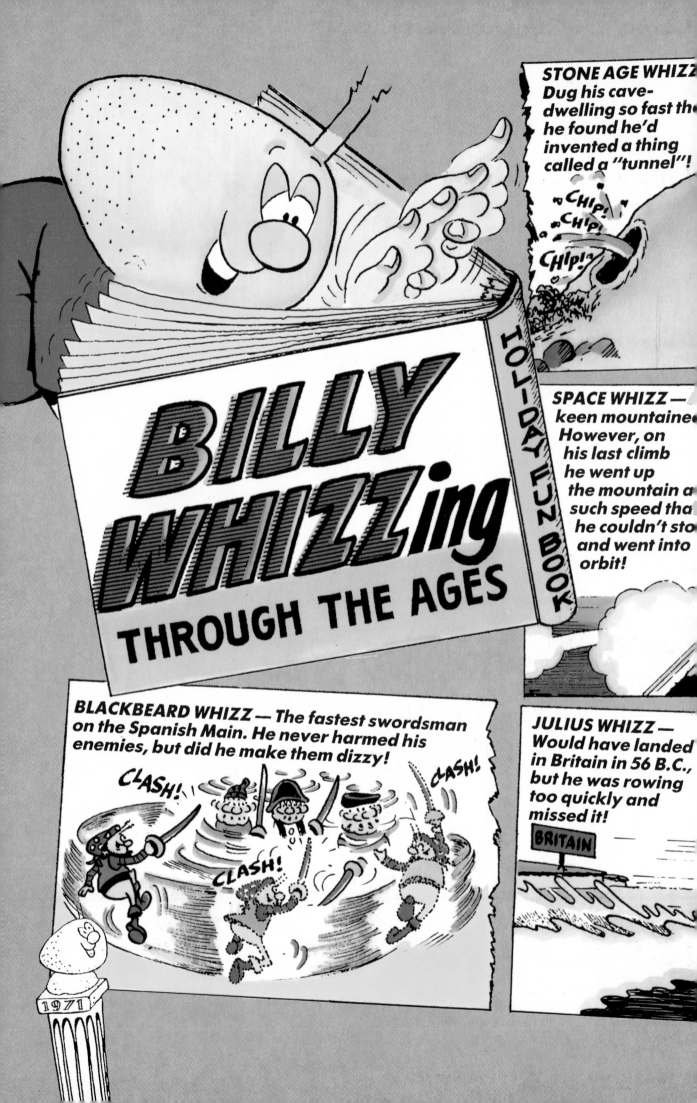